ISBN 0 86112 915 6
© Brimax Books Ltd 1993. All rights reserved.
Published by Brimax Books Ltd, Newmarket, England 1993.
This edition published 1995.
Printed in China.

CHRISTMAS STORYBOOK

Illustrated by Stephanie Ryder

Brimax . Newmarket . England

The NIGHT Before CHRISTMAS

'Twas the night before Christmas,
When all through the house
Not a creature was stirring,
Not even a mouse;
The stockings were hung
By the chimney with care,
In hopes that St Nicholas
Soon would be there;
The children were nestled
All snug in their beds,
While visions of sugar plums
Danced in their heads.

And Mamma in her 'kerchief,
And I in my cap,
Had just settled our brains
For a long winter's nap,
When out on the lawn
There arose such a clatter,
I sprang from the bed
To see what was the matter.
Away to the window
I flew like a flash,
Tore open the shutters
And threw up the sash.

11

The moon, on the breast
Of the new fallen snow,
Gave the lustre of mid-day
To objects below,
When what to my wondering
Eyes should appear,
But a miniature sleigh,
And eight tiny reindeer,
With a little old driver,
So lively and quick,
I knew in a moment
It must be St Nick.

13

More rapid than eagles
His coursers they came,
And he whistled and shouted,
And called them by name;
"Now, Dasher! Now, Dancer!
Now, Prancer and Vixen!
On, Comet! On, Cupid!
On, Donner and Blitzen
To the top of the porch!
To the top of the wall!
Now, dash away! Dash away!
Dash away all!"

As dry leaves that before
The wild hurricane fly,
When they meet with an obstacle,
Mount to the sky;
So up to the housetop
The coursers they flew,
With the sleigh full of toys,
And St Nicholas too.

And then, in a twinkling,
I heard on the roof
The prancing and pawing
Of each little hoof –
As I drew in my head,
And was turning around,
Down the chimney St Nicholas
Came with a bound.

19

He was dressed all in fur,
From his head to his foot,
And his clothes were all tarnished
With ashes and soot;
A bundle of toys he had
Flung on his back,
And he looked like a pedlar
Just opening his pack.
His eyes – how they twinkled!
His dimples, how merry!
His cheeks were like roses,
His nose like a cherry.

His droll little mouth
Was drawn up like a bow,
And the beard of his chin
Was as white as the snow;
The stump of his pipe he held
Tight in his teeth,
And the smoke it encircled
His head like a wreath;
He had a broad face
And a little round belly
That shook, when he laughed,
Like a bowlful of jelly.

He was chubby and plump,
A right jolly old elf,
And I laughed, when I saw him,
In spite of myself;
A wink of his eye
And a twist of his head,
Soon gave me to know
I had nothing to dread;
He spoke not a word,
But went straight to his work,
And filled all the stockings;
Then turned with a jerk,

25

And laying his finger
Aside of his nose,
And giving a nod,
Up the chimney he rose;
He sprang to his sleigh,
To his team gave a whistle,
And away they all flew
Like the down of a thistle.
But I heard him exclaim,
Ere he drove out of sight,
"Happy Christmas to all,
And to all a good night."

Clement C Moore

Jingle bells! Jingle bells!
Jingle all the way,
Oh, what fun it is to ride
In a one-horse open sleigh.

Dashing through the snow,
In a one-horse open sleigh,
Merrily we go,
Laughing all the way.

Bells on bob-sleigh ring,
Making spirits bright,
Oh, what fun it is to ride
In a one-horse sleigh tonight.

Jingle bells! Jingle bells!
Jingle all the way,
Oh, what fun it is to ride
In a one-horse open sleigh.

Traditional

Say these words again.

moon	snow
chimney	plump
window	reindeer
whistled	house
sleigh	soot
roof	teeth
bundle	twinkled

What can you see?

sleigh

reindeer

stocking

toys

Christmas tree

36

A VERY SPECIAL CHRISTMAS TREE

It was Christmas Eve and Tinker the Squirrel was tucked up warm and snug in his little home in the big oak tree. He was staring at one of the pictures in his book. "Oh dear," he sighed as he shut the book.

39

Just then Mrs Rabbit was hopping by and heard Tinker sigh. Mrs Rabbit liked Tinker and knew how cheerful he usually was. It was very unlike him to sigh.

"What is the matter, Tinker?"
she called softly.
Tinker looked out of his hole.
"I have just seen the most
beautiful Christmas tree in my
book. It was covered with
shiny balls and pretty lights
that twinkled like stars."

Tinker showed Mrs Rabbit the picture in his book.
"It is beautiful," said Mrs Rabbit.
"I wish I had a tree like that instead of my dull brown one," said Tinker.

"Never mind Tinker," said
Mrs Rabbit. "It will soon be
Spring again and your tree
will be covered in beautiful
green leaves."
"Yes, you are right," said
Tinker. "But I still wish it
was prettier for Christmas."

"You should go to sleep now," said Mrs Rabbit. "Tomorrow is Christmas Day."
Mrs Rabbit hopped away. She did not like to see her friend so upset at Christmas time. She wondered if there was anything she could do to help.

On her way home she met Herbert Hare, Freddie Fieldmouse and Daisy Dormouse. She told them all about the tree in Tinker's book and how unhappy Tinker was that his tree was all bare.

"He is such a good little squirrel," said Mrs Rabbit. "It would be lovely if we could make his Christmas rather special."

"But how?" Freddie and Herbert said together.

"I have an idea," said Mrs Rabbit. "Come with me."

The next morning was Christmas
Day and Tinker was awakened by
a great deal of whispering. He
crept out of his hole to see
what all the noise was about.
All his friends were gathered
around the foot of the tree.

"Happy Christmas, Tinker," they all cried.
Tinker looked all around him and could hardly believe his eyes. While he had been asleep, his friends had been very busy.

They had been collecting pine cones, berries, nuts, mistletoe and holly, while some spiders had been spinning some delicate webs. When everything had been gathered together the animals started to decorate the tree.

All the gifts were hung from
the branches and the tree no
longer looked dull and bare.
As the snow began to fall the
tree sparkled brightly.

"It is beautiful," said Tinker. "Much more beautiful than the tree in my book. Thank you all so much. This is the best Christmas present I have ever had."

Say these words again.

tucked   snug
staring   sigh
matter   shiny
instead   leaves
hopped   friend
unhappy   lovely
gathered   believe

Who can you see?

Tinker

Mrs Rabbit

Herbert Hare

Freddie Fieldmouse

Daisy Dormouse

THE CHRISTMAS TEDDY BEAR

Bobby Bear lived by himself
in the forest. It was Christmas
Eve but Bobby Bear was unhappy.
His house was old and very
cold. There were holes in the
roof and some of the windows
were broken.

"This house is falling down,"
said Bobby Bear. "I must find
somewhere nice to live for
Christmas."

He packed his clothes and his toothbrush and began his search for a new home. It started to snow.

"I must find a new home soon," said Bobby Bear.

Rosie Robin flew down beside him.

"You can share my nest until Spring," she said.

"Thank you, Rosie," said Bobby, "But I am far too big."

Bobby Bear saw a little house in the bushes.

"Hello," he said. "I am looking for somewhere to live."

"I live here with my five children," said Poppy Fox. "Gertie Goose lives all alone. You should try there. If you go straight ahead and turn left at the big tree you will come to a bridge. You should see Gertie's house from there."

"Thank you," said Bobby.

It began to snow harder and Bobby Bear couldn't remember whether he should have turned left or right at the tree. He saw a house and knocked on the door.

"Can you tell me where Gertie Goose's house is?" he asked.

"Turn left here," said Ben Rabbit, "until you come to the bridge. You will see Gertie's house from there."

"Thank you," said Bobby.

Bobby Bear turned left but the snow started to fall heavily. Bobby could not see where he was going. He could not find the bridge. He was lost.

"Oh no!" said Bobby. "It is very cold and I have nowhere to live, I cannot find Gertie Goose's house. What am I going to do?"

Bobby continued walking, hoping that he would find the bridge soon.

It began to get dark. Bobby Bear walked on feeling very cold and very tired. Then, under the fir trees, he saw the biggest house he had ever seen. It had candles in the windows and a big Christmas tree by the door.

"What a lovely house," said Bobby Bear. "This is where I would like to stay for Christmas."

The door was open and Bobby Bear walked inside. No one seemed to be at home. Bobby Bear looked around. There were toys everywhere. He saw train sets, puzzles and toy cars. There were dolls, games and books. There was even a big rocking-horse. The house was just full of toys.

81

Bobby Bear was very tired so
he sat on a sofa in front of
the fire.
"Don't you know who lives
here?" said a little mouse,
who lived under the sofa.
"No, I don't," said Bobby Bear
in a sleepy voice.
"Santa lives here," said the
little mouse.
But Bobby Bear said nothing.
He was fast asleep!

That night, Santa filled his sleigh with toys and gave his reindeer a big supper. Bobby Bear was still fast asleep. Santa picked him up and put him on the sleigh next to three dolls and a big toy rabbit. It was still snowing as they set off through the forest to deliver the toys.

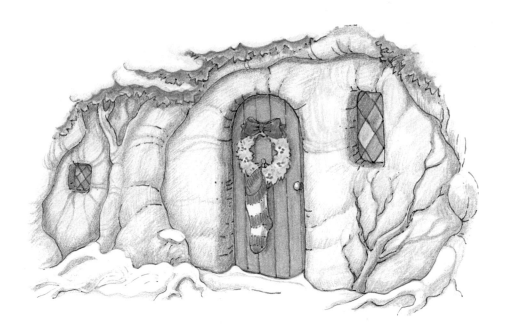

At her house, Gertie Goose hung her stocking by her bed. Poppy Fox and her babies hung their stocking on the door. At his house, Ben Rabbit and his brothers and sisters hung a little sack beside the Christmas tree. They were very excited when they went to bed, but they were all fast asleep when Santa crept into their houses with their presents.

Soon it was Christmas morning and Bobby Bear woke up after his long sleep.

"Where am I?" he said, looking all around him.

He was in a Christmas stocking by Gertie Goose's bed. Gertie woke up.

"How lovely!" she cried. "Santa has left a teddy bear in my stocking!"

Bobby Bear kept very still as Gertie gave him a big hug.

Gertie's friends arrived for
her party.
"Merry Christmas!" said Gertie.
"Look at my lovely teddy bear."
But Bobby Bear's nose started
to tickle.
"Atishoo!" he sneezed.
"Teddy bears cannot sneeze!"
said Poppy Fox.
"It's me!" said Bobby Bear.
"I fell asleep in Santa's house
and he thought I was a teddy
bear!"

The party was over and Gertie's house was very quiet.

"What a lovely party," said Bobby Bear.

Gertie had learned that Bobby Bear had no home.

"You can live with me now," she said. "I have a spare room and I get lonely by myself."

"Thank you, Gertie," said Bobby Bear. "Santa has given both of us a present. You have a new friend and I have a new home."

Say these words again.

lived	forest
clothes	toothbrush
house	bushes
snow	harder
somewhere	friends
began	dark
spare	present

Who can you see?

Bobby Bear

Poppy Fox

Rosie Robin

Ben Rabbit

Gertie Goose

The CHRISTMAS Story

Long ago, in a town called Nazareth, there lived a young woman named Mary. One day a great light appeared and the angel Gabriel stood before her. "Do not be afraid," said the angel. "I bring you joyful news. God has chosen you to be the mother of his son. You will have a baby and you must call him Jesus."

In the same town there lived a carpenter named Joseph. Joseph loved Mary very much. He was going to marry her. The angel came to visit Joseph and told him that Mary was going to have God's son. Later Joseph came to see Mary and told her what the angel had said.

One day a message came from the governor of the land. All of the people had to go back to the place where they had been born so they could be counted. Joseph was worried. He and Mary would have to go to Bethlehem. This was a long way away and Mary was almost ready to have her baby.

103

They set off early the next morning. Joseph led the way. Mary rode on a donkey. The road was long and hard. They didn't reach Bethlehem until the evening. The town was full of people. Joseph tried everywhere to find a place to stay, but all the rooms were taken. Mary was so tired she could hardly stay awake.

At last an innkeeper said, "All my rooms are full, but you can use my stable. It is clean and warm in there."
Joseph thanked him and they went inside. All around them cows and donkeys lay peacefully asleep. The hay was soft and smelled sweet. Mary and Joseph lay down and rested.

In the night, Mary gave birth
to her baby. It was a boy as
the angel had said. They
named him Jesus.
Mary wrapped him in
a blanket and laid him in
a manger, where it was soft
and warm.
Mary and Joseph watched over
Jesus lovingly. They knew he
was a very special baby.

Out on the hillside above the town, some shepherds were looking after their sheep. Suddenly the sky was filled with light and an angel appeared. The shepherds fell to the ground in fear.

But the angel said, "Do not be afraid. I bring you good news. Today a child is born. He is the son of God. You will find him in Bethlehem, lying in a manger."

The shepherds gazed in wonder as the sky was filled with angels singing.

"We must go and find this child," said one. "We can take one of our newborn lambs as a gift."

They went to Bethlehem and found Jesus in the stable with Mary and Joseph. They fell to their knees and offered their gift.

Far away in an eastern land lived some wise men. One night they saw a bright new star in the sky. They wanted to know what it meant. They looked in their books for the answer. "It means that a new king has been born," they said. "We must go and look for him so that we can worship him. The star will guide us."

The wise men set off on their journey. The star shone brightly in front of them by day and by night. They came to the palace of King Herod who said to them, "You must find the new king then tell me where he is." King Herod was not very pleased.

The wise men followed the star for many miles. It stopped right over the stable where Jesus lay. "We are looking for the newborn king," they said. "A bright star has guided us from far away." Joseph led them into the stable. They knelt before Jesus and offered him some very special gifts of gold, frankincense and myrrh.

The next day, the wise men set out for King Herod's palace. They stopped to rest and while they were asleep an angel came to them in a dream. "Do not go back to Herod," the angel warned. "He does not want Jesus to be King." The wise men decided to go home a different way.

Mary and Joseph were very happy and proud. They knew their baby was really the son of God. They knew he was very special and that he would have important work to do when he grew up. They also knew that Jesus would be loved throughout the world and that people would remember his birth as a time of happiness and peace.

Say these words again.

carpenter	star
message	palace
donkey	special
stable	dream
blanket	happiness
sheep	bright
gift	worship

Who can you see?

Jesus

Mary

Joseph

shepherd

wise men